Do The Math™

Created by
Marilyn Burns

✕ **Multiplication** Ⓒ

Factors greater than 12

··

WorkSpace

Cover photo: © Frans Lemmens/Getty Images.

No part of this publication may be reproduced in whole or in part, or stored in a retrieval system, or transmitted in any form or by any means, electronic, mechanical, photocopying, recording, or otherwise, without written permission of the publisher. For information regarding permission, write to Scholastic Inc., Education Group, 557 Broadway, New York, NY 10012.

Copyright © 2008 by Scholastic Inc.

All rights reserved.   Published by Scholastic Inc.   Printed in the U.S.A.

ISBN 978-0-545-02241-5

SCHOLASTIC, DO THE MATH, and associated logos and designs are trademarks and/or registered trademarks of Scholastic Inc.

1   2   3   4   5   6   7   8   9   10   40   16 15 14 13 12 11 10 09 08 07

Multiply by 12

1

How many eggs fit in 3 cartons?

$3 \times 12 = $ _____

2

10	2
10	2
10	2

Split the cartons into 10s and 2s.

3

$3 \times 10 = 30$
$3 \times 2 = 6$
$30 + 6 = 36$
$3 \times 12 = 36$

Write equations to solve the problem.

---

1 How many eggs fit in 4 cartons?

$4 \times 12 = $ _____

_____
_____
_____

2 How many eggs fit in 7 cartons?

$7 \times 12 = $ _____

_____
_____
_____

3 How many eggs fit in 8 cartons?

$8 \times 12 = $ _____

_____
_____
_____

4 How many eggs fit in 9 cartons?

$9 \times 12 = $ _____

_____
_____
_____

Home Note: Your child uses the number-splitting strategy to multiply by 12.

Multiply by 10

DIRECTIONS

1	2	3
15×10	$15 \times 10 = \underline{\ 150\ }$ Tack on a zero.	10, 20, 30, 40, 50, 60, 70, 80, 90, 100, 110, 120, 130, 140, 150 Count by 10s.

	Tack on a zero	Count by 10s
① 18×10	$18 \times 10 = \underline{\qquad}$	
② 12×10	$12 \times 10 = \underline{\qquad}$	
③ 16×10	$16 \times 10 = \underline{\qquad}$	
④ 19×10	$19 \times 10 = \underline{\qquad}$	
⑤ 13×10	$13 \times 10 = \underline{\qquad}$	

Home Note: Your child uses two ways to multiply by 10.

Three-Factor Problems

1

$$3 \times 2 \times 3$$

2

$$3 \times 2 \times 3$$
$$6 \times 3 = 18$$

$$3 \times 2 \times 3$$
$$9 \times 2 = 18$$

$$3 \times 2 \times 3$$
$$3 \times 6 = 18$$

Write and solve three two-factor problems.

$$2 \times 2 \times 4$$

Lesson 3

Home Note: Your child uses the Associative Property of Multiplication to solve a problem three ways.

TM & © Scholastic Inc. All rights reserved

More Three-Factor Problems

1

$3 \times 2 \times 3$

2

$3 \times 2 \times 3$
$6 \times 3 = 18$

$3 \times 2 \times 3$
$9 \times 2 = 18$

$3 \times 2 \times 3$
$3 \times 6 = 18$

Write and solve three two-factor problems.

① $2 \times 5 \times 4$

② $2 \times 6 \times 4$

③ $5 \times 2 \times 3$

Home Note: Your child uses the Associative Property
of Multiplication to solve problems three ways.

Lesson 3

5

TM & © Scholastic Inc. All rights reserved.

Solving Three-Factor Problems

1

$$3 \times 2 \times 3$$

2

$$3 \times 2 \times 3$$
$$6 \times 3 = 18$$

$$3 \times 2 \times 3$$
$$9 \times 2 = 18$$

$$3 \times 2 \times 3$$
$$3 \times 6 = 18$$

Write and solve three two-factor problems.

① $2 \times 5 \times 3$

② $2 \times 5 \times 7$

③ $2 \times 5 \times 5$

④ $2 \times 8 \times 5$

Lesson 4

Home Note: Your child uses the Associative Property of Multiplication to solve problems three ways.

TM & © Scholastic Inc. All rights reserved

Show What You Know

➤ Solve by splitting into 10s and 2s.

① How many eggs fit in 6 cartons?

$6 \times 12 =$ _____

② How many eggs fit in 8 cartons?

$8 \times 12 =$ _____

➤ Solve each problem two ways.

	Tack on a zero	Count by 10s
③ 17×10	$17 \times 10 =$ _____	
④ 14×10	$14 \times 10 =$ _____	

Home Note: Your child multiplies by 12 and by 10.

Show What You Know

1

$$3 \times 2 \times 3$$

2

$3 \times 2 \times 3$
$6 \times 3 = 18$

$3 \times 2 \times 3$
$9 \times 2 = 18$

$3 \times 2 \times 3$
$3 \times 6 = 18$

Write and solve three two-factor problems.

① $5 \times 2 \times 9$

② $2 \times 5 \times 8$

③ $6 \times 2 \times 5$

Home Note: Your child solves multiplication problems three ways.

Multiply by 11

DIRECTIONS

1

$5 \times 11 = $ _____

2

10	1
10	1
10	1
10	1
10	1

Split the 11s into 10s and 1s.

3

$5 \times 10 = 50$
$5 \times 1 = 5$
$50 + 5 = 55$
$5 \times 11 = 55$

Write equations to solve the problem.

① $2 \times 11 = $ _____

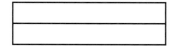

_____
_____
_____
_____

② $4 \times 11 = $ _____

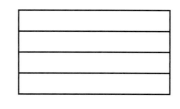

_____
_____
_____
_____

TM & © Scholastic Inc. All rights reserved.

③ 7 × 11 = _____

④ 11 × 11 = _____

Home Note: Your child uses the number-splitting strategy to multiply by 11.

TM & © Scholastic Inc. All rights reserved

Use the Splitting Strategy

DIRECTIONS

1

16×4

2

$10 \times 4 = 40$
$6 \times 4 = 24$
$40 + 24 = 64$
$16 \times 4 = 64$

Use splitting, and write equations to solve the problem.

5×18

Home Note: Your child uses the splitting strategy to solve a multiplication problem.

Lesson 7   11

Use the Splitting Strategy

1

$$16 \times 4$$

2

$10 \times 4 = 40$

$6 \times 4 = 24$

$40 + 24 = 64$

$16 \times 4 = 64$

Use splitting, and write equations to solve the problem.

① 4×13

② 15×7

③ 2×19

④ 14×7

Home Note: Your child uses the splitting strategy to solve multiplication problems.

More Practice Using the Splitting Strategy

DIRECTIONS

1

8 × 14

2

$8 \times 10 = 80$
$8 \times 4 = 32$
$80 + 32 = 112$
$8 \times 14 = 112$

Use splitting, and write equations to solve the problem.

① 9 × 17

② 4 × 19

③ 16 × 7

④ 4 × 18

Home Note: Your child uses the splitting strategy to solve multiplication problems.

Game Rules for Pathways

What you need

• *Pathways Game Board* A
• dry erase marker and eraser

1

Pathways Game Board Ⓐ

18	32	24	15	48
28	40	35	64	20
30	12	56	21	16
9	25	49	42	36

③ 4 5 ⑥ 7 8

Player X marks two factors, and draws an X on the product.

2

Pathways Game Board Ⓐ

18	32	24	15	48
28	40	35	64	20
30	12	56	21	16
9	25	49	42	36

③ 4 5 ⑥ 7 8

Player X	Player O
$3 \times 6 = 18$	

Player O checks that the product is correct.
Both players write the equation.

3

Pathways Game Board Ⓐ

18	32	㉔	15	48
28	40	35	64	20
30	12	56	21	16
9	25	49	42	36

3 ④ 5 ⑥ 7 8

Player X	Player O
$3 \times 6 = 18$	$4 \times 6 = 24$

Player O marks one new factor, and draws a O on the product.
Player X checks the product, and both
players write the equation.

➤ The winner is the first player to complete a path from top
to bottom or from side to side of the game board.

  **Home Note:** Your child practices multiplication
facts and strategic thinking by playing a game.

Pathways

➤ Record your equations and your partner's equations.

Player X	Player O

Home Note: Your child practices multiplication facts and strategic thinking by playing a game.

TM & © Scholastic Inc. All rights reserved.

Pathways

➤ Record your equations and your partner's equations.

Player X	Player O

Home Note: Your child practices multiplication facts and strategic thinking by playing a game.

TM & © Scholastic Inc. All rights reserved

Show What You Know

DIRECTIONS

1

16×4

2

$10 \times 4 = 40$
$6 \times 4 = 24$
$40 + 24 = 64$
$16 \times 4 = 64$

Use splitting, and write equations to solve the problem.

① 11×8

② 18×3

③ 5×15

④ 19×9

⑤ 14 × 5

⑥ 6 × 16

⑦ 17 × 8

⑧ 13 × 6

⑨ 7 × 18

⑩ 16 × 6

Home Note: Your child uses the splitting strategy to solve multiplication problems.

Times 10

➤ Record your equations and your partner's equations.

Player X	Player O

TM & © Scholastic Inc. All rights reserved.

Home Note: Your child practices multiplying by 10 by playing a game.

Game Rules for Times 10

What you need

• *Pathways Game Board* A

• dry erase marker and eraser

1

Times 10 Game Board Ⓐ

90	450	300	810	200
180	630	540	350	250
240	150	2̶1̶0̶	270	360
420	280	160	490	120

③ 4 5 6 ⑦ 9

Player X marks two factors, and finds the product.
Then Player X multiplies the product by 10
and draws an X on that square.

2

Times 10 Game Board Ⓐ

90	450	300	810	200
180	630	540	350	250
240	150	2̶1̶0̶	270	360
420	280	160	490	120

③ 4 5 6 ⑦ 9

Player X	Player O
$3 \times 7 = 21$	
$21 \times 10 = 210$	

Player O checks that the product is correct.
Both players write the equations.

3

Times 10 Game Board Ⓐ

90	450	300	810	200
180	630	540	350	250
240	150	2̶1̶0̶	270	360
420	⑱280	160	490	120

3 ④ 5 6 ⑦ 9

Player X	Player O
$3 \times 7 = 21$	$4 \times 7 = 28$
$21 \times 10 = 210$	$28 \times 10 = 280$

Player O marks one new factor, and multiplies the product
of the factors by 10. Player O draws an O on the square.
Player X checks the product. Both players write the equations.

➤ **The winner is the first player to complete a path from top
to bottom or from side to side of the game board.**

Home Note: Your child practices multiplying by 10 by playing a game.

TM & © Scholastic Inc. All rights reserved.

Times 10

➤ Record your equations and your partner's equations.

Player X	Player O

TM & © Scholastic Inc. All rights reserved.

Home Note: Your child practices multiplying by 10 by playing a game.

Times 10

➤ Record your equations and your partner's equations.

Player X	Player O

Home Note: Your child practices multiplying by 10 by playing a game.

TM & © Scholastic Inc. All rights reserved.

Write a Two-Factor Problem as a Three-Factor Problem

DIRECTIONS

1

7×40

$7 \times 4 \times 10$

Rewrite one factor so that you have the factor 10.

2

7×40

$7 \times 4 \times 10$

$28 \times 10 = 280$

Multiply by 10 last.

3

7×40

$7 \times 4 \times 10$

$28 \times 10 = 280$

$7 \times 40 = 280$

Write the original problem with the product.

6×70

Home Note: Your child rewrites a two-factor problem as a three-factor problem and solves it.

Write Two-Factor Problems as Three-Factor Problems

DIRECTIONS

1

$$7 \times 40$$

$$7 \times 4 \times 10$$

Rewrite one factor so that you have the factor 10.

2

$$7 \times 40$$

$$7 \times 4 \times 10$$

$$28 \times 10 = 280$$

Multiply by 10 last.

3

$$7 \times 40$$

$$7 \times 4 \times 10$$

$$28 \times 10 = 280$$

$$7 \times 40 = 280$$

Write the original problem with the product.

① 8×20

___ × ___ × ___

② 8×70

___ × ___ × ___

③ 3×50

___ × ___ × ___

④ 5×90

___ × ___ × ___

⑤ 70 × 3

___ × ___ × ___

⑥ 80 × 9

⑦ 9 × 90

⑧ 80 × 4

⑨ 30 × 8

⑩ 60 × 7

Home Note: Your child rewrites two-factor problems as three-factor problems and solves them.

Lesson 13

25

TM & © Scholastic Inc. All rights reserved.

Game Rules for Target 300

What you need
- red number cube (1–6)
- *WorkSpace* page 27

➤ **A game is six turns.**

1

Player A rolls the number cube.

2

Player A	Score	Player B	Score
2 × 20 2 × 2 × 10 4 × 10 = 40	40		

Player A multiplies the number by 10, 20, 30, 40, or 50.
Both players record the solution and score.

3

Player B rolls the number cube.

4

Player A	Score	Player B	Score
2 × 20 2 × 2 × 10 4 × 10 = 40	40	5 × 20 5 × 2 × 10 10 × 10 = 100	100

Player B multiplies the number by 10, 20, 30, 40, or 50.
Both players record the equation and score.

➤ **Players add their amounts from each turn to their previous scores.**

➤ **The winner is the player whose score is closer to 300 after 6 turns.**

Home Note: Your child practices multiplying by multiples of 10 by playing a game.

TM & © Scholastic Inc. All rights reserved.

Target 300

➤ Record your equations and scores and your partner's equations and scores.

Player A	Score	Player B	Score

_____ is _____ points from 300.

_____ is _____ points from 300.

_____ won the game.

 Home Note: Your child practices multiplying by multiples of 10 by playing a game.

Target 300

➤ Record your equations and scores and your partner's equations and scores.

Player A	Score	Player B	Score

_____ is _____ points from 300.

_____ is _____ points from 300.

_____ won the game.

 Home Note: Your child practices multiplying by multiples of 10 by playing a game.

Show What You Know

DIRECTIONS

1	2	3
7×40 $7 \times 4 \times 10$ Rewrite one factor so that you have the factor 10.	7×40 $7 \times 4 \times 10$ $28 \times 10 = 280$ Multiply by 10 last.	7×40 $7 \times 4 \times 10$ $28 \times 10 = 280$ $7 \times 40 = 280$ Write the original problem with the product.

① 90×7

② 80×6

③ 8×70

④ 40×5

⑤ 4×90

⑥ 3×70

Home Note: Your child multiplies one-digit factors by multiples of 10.

Show What You Know

① $10 \times 42 =$ _____

② $23 \times 10 =$ _____

③ $55 \times 10 =$ _____

④ $10 \times 39 =$ _____

⑤ $77 \times 10 =$ _____

⑥ $86 \times 10 =$ _____

⑦ $10 \times 34 =$ _____

⑧ $41 \times 10 =$ _____

⑨ $98 \times 10 =$ _____

⑩ $10 \times 62 =$ _____

Target 300

➤ Record your equations and scores and your partner's equations and scores.

Player A	Score	Player B	Score

_____ is _____ points from 300.

_____ is _____ points from 300.

_____ won the game.

 Home Note: Your child practices multiplying by multiples of 10 by playing a game.

TM & © Scholastic Inc. All rights reserved.

The Shortcut

➤ **Write each product.**

(1) $20 \times 9 =$ _____

(2) $4 \times 50 =$ _____

(3) $9 \times 30 =$ _____

(4) $7 \times 80 =$ _____

(5) $60 \times 7 =$ _____

(6) $80 \times 4 =$ _____

(7) $50 \times 6 =$ _____

(8) $4 \times 30 =$ _____

(9) $60 \times 9 =$ _____

(10) $40 \times 9 =$ _____

(11) $3 \times 50 =$ _____

(12) $90 \times 6 =$ _____

Home Note: Your child multiplies one-digit factors by multiples of 10.

TM & © Scholastic Inc. All rights reserved

Use the Splitting Strategy

1

54×7

2

$54 = 50 + 4$

$50 \times 7 = 350$ 350

$4 \times 7 = 28$ $+28$

                   378

$54 \times 7 = 378$

Solve by splitting.

---

① 93×7

② 82×5

③ 17×6

④ 48×8

Home Note: Your child uses the splitting strategy to solve multiplication problems.

Make Estimates to Check Products

DIRECTIONS

1

$$58 \times 7$$

$$60 \times 7 = 420$$

Make an estimate.

2

$58 = 50 + 8$

$50 \times 7 = 350 \qquad 350$

$8 \times 7 = 56 \qquad \underline{+56}$

$\qquad\qquad\qquad 406$

$58 \times 7 = 406$

Use the splitting strategy
to solve the problem.

3

✓

Write a
check mark
if your answer
is close to
your estimate.

Make an estimate	Solve the problem	Check estimate
① 89×4		
② 21×3		
③ 49×6		

 Home Note: Your child makes estimates to check the reasonableness of products.

Solve 37 × 6

DIRECTIONS

1

$$58$$
$$\times\ 7$$

$$60 \times 7 = 420$$

Make an estimate.

2

$$58 = 50 + 8$$
$$58$$
$$\times\ 7$$
$$50 \times 7 = \overline{350}$$
$$8 \times 7 = \ \underline{56}$$
$$406$$

Solve the problem.

3

✓

Write a check mark if your answer is close to your estimate.

My estimate

_____

Is your answer reasonable? _____

Home Note: Your child makes an estimate to check the reasonableness of a product.

Lesson 19

35

Make Estimates to Check Products

1

$$58$$
$$\times 7$$

$$60 \times 7 = 420$$

Make an estimate.

2

$$58 = 50 + 8$$
$$58$$
$$\times 7$$
$$50 \times 7 = 350$$
$$8 \times 7 = 56$$
$$406$$

Solve the problem.

3

✓

Write a check mark if your answer is close to your estimate.

Make an estimate	Solve the problem	Check estimate
① $\begin{array}{r} 75 \\ \times 9 \end{array}$		
② $\begin{array}{r} 92 \\ \times 8 \end{array}$		
③ $\begin{array}{r} 55 \\ \times 5 \end{array}$		
④ $\begin{array}{r} 48 \\ \times 9 \end{array}$		

Home Note: Your child makes estimates to check the reasonableness of products.

Show What You Know

DIRECTIONS

➤ Write each product.

① 6 × 40 = _____

② 5 × 90 = _____

③ 18 × 10 = _____

④ 50 × 4 = _____

⑤ 70 × 6 = _____

⑥ 2 × 30 = _____

⑦ 3 × 80 = _____

⑧ 7 × 20 = _____

⑨ 30 × 9 = _____

⑩ 7 × 50 = _____

⑪ 8 × 60 = _____

⑫ 90 × 4 = _____

⑬ 70 × 2 = _____

⑭ 5 × 80 = _____

⑮ 9 × 70 = _____

⑯ 60 × 6 = _____

Home Note: Your child multiplies by multiples of 10 and uses the splitting strategy to solve problems.

Show What You Know

1

$$58$$
$$\times\ 7$$

$$60 \times 7 = 420$$

Make an estimate.

2

$$58 = 50 + 8$$
$$58$$
$$\times 7$$
$$50 \times 7 = \overline{350}$$
$$8 \times 7 = \underline{\ 56}$$
$$406$$

Solve the problem.

3

Write a check mark if your answer is close to your estimate.

Make an estimate	Solve the problem	Check estimate
① $\begin{array}{r} 78 \\ \times\ 3 \end{array}$		
② $\begin{array}{r} 81 \\ \times\ 7 \end{array}$		
③ $\begin{array}{r} 58 \\ \times\ 4 \end{array}$		
④ $\begin{array}{r} 36 \\ \times\ 9 \end{array}$		

38 Lesson 20   **Home Note:** Your child makes estimates to check the reasonableness of products.

TM & © Scholastic Inc. All rights reserved.

Target 1000

DIRECTIONS

➤ Multiply the number you roll by 10, 20, 40, 60, or 80.

➤ Record your equations and scores and your partner's equations and scores.

Player A	Score	Player B	Score

_____ is _____ points from 1000.

_____ is _____ points from 1000.

_____ won the game.

Home Note: Your child practices multiplying by multiples of 10 by playing a game.

Multiply by Multiples of 100

➤ Write each product.

(1) 2 × 300 = _____

(2) 900 × 4 = _____

(3) 400 × 7 = _____

(4) 500 × 9 = _____

(5) 200 × 9 = _____

(6) 300 × 8 = _____

(7) 6 × 700 = _____

(8) 6 × 800 = _____

(9) 4 × 300 = _____

(10) 300 × 7 = _____

(11) 3 × 600 = _____

(12) 700 × 8 = _____

(13) 800 × 2 = _____

(14) 5 × 400 = _____

(15) 8 × 200 = _____

(16) 400 × 4 = _____

Home Note: Your child multiplies by multiples of 100.

TM & © Scholastic Inc. All rights reserved

Solve 321 × 5

321
× 5

Make an estimate.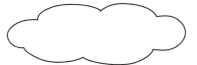

Split 321 into its place-value parts. _____ = _____ + _____ + _____

Write three multiplication equations and add the products.

_____ × _____ = _____

_____ × _____ = _____

_____ × _____ = _____

_____

321 × 5 = _____

Is your product close to your estimate? _____

Home Note: Your child multiplies a three-digit factor by a one-digit factor.

Lesson 22   41

Make Estimates to Check Products

1

$$\begin{array}{r} 439 \\ \times \quad 5 \end{array}$$

$400 \times 5 = 2000$

Make an estimate.

2

$400 \times 5 = 2000$
$30 \times 5 = \quad 150$
$9 \times 5 = \quad \underline{45}$
$\qquad \quad 2195$

Multiply and add.

3

✓

Write a check mark if your answer is close to your estimate.

Make an estimate	Multiply and add	Check estimate
① $\begin{array}{r} 278 \\ \times \ 8 \end{array}$		
② $\begin{array}{r} 781 \\ \times \ 3 \end{array}$		
③ $\begin{array}{r} 864 \\ \times \ 5 \end{array}$		
④ $\begin{array}{r} 614 \\ \times \ 9 \end{array}$		
⑤ $\begin{array}{r} 583 \\ \times \ 6 \end{array}$		

Home Note: Your child multiplies three-digit factors by one-digit factors.

Product Roll

DIRECTIONS

➤ Record your work.
➤ Check your partner's work.

Numbers rolled   ____ ____ ____ ____

Possible problems   ×____   ×____   ×____   ×____

Estimates   _____ _____ _____ _____

Multiplication problem   ____ ____ ____

    × _____ ____
    _____

_____ =

_____ =

_____ = _____

Home Note: Your child practices multiplying three-digit factors by one-digit factors by playing a game.

Lesson 23

43

Game Rules for Product Roll

What you need

- two number cubes (0–5)
- two number cubes (4–9)
- *WorkSpace* page 43 or 45

➤ **Each player follows the steps shown.**

1

Roll all four number cubes.

2

Arrange the numbers and estimate the products.

543	541	531	431
× 1	× 3	× 4	× 5

Estimates:

$500 \times 1 = 500$ $500 \times 3 = 1500$ $500 \times 4 = 2000$ $400 \times 5 = 2000$

3

Choose the problem you think has the greatest product.
Use splitting to find the product.

$$
\begin{array}{ccc}
4 & 3 & 1 \\
\times & & 5 \\
\end{array}
$$

$400 \times 5 = 2000$
$30 \times 5 = 150$
$1 \times 5 = 5$
2155

4

Check your partner's work. The player with
the greater product draws a star next to it.

➤ **The winner is the player whose product is greater.**

 Home Note: Your child practices multiplying three-digit
factors by one-digit factors by playing a game.

Product Roll

DIRECTIONS

➤ Record your work.

➤ Check your partner's work.

Numbers rolled   _____   _____   _____   _____

Possible problems   × _____   × _____   × _____   × _____

Estimates   _____   _____   _____   _____

Multiplication problem   _____ _____ _____

              ×   _____

       _____ =

       _____ =

       _____ = _____

Home Note: Your child practices multiplying three-digit factors by one-digit factors by playing a game.

Lesson 23

45

Multiply Multiples of 10

DIRECTIONS

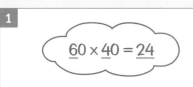

1

60 × 40

$60 \times 40 = 24$

Think 6 × 4 = 24.

2

$60 \times 40 = 2400$

Think times 10, tack on a zero;
times 10, tack on another zero.

① 20 × 40 = _____

② 60 × 50 = _____

③ 90 × 40 = _____

④ 30 × 60 = _____

⑤ 80 × 70 = _____

⑥ 90 × 70 = _____

⑦ 50 × 80 = _____

⑧ 20 × 80 = _____

⑨ 20 × 20 = _____

⑩ 60 × 80 = _____

⑪ 40 × 70 = _____

⑫ 30 × 90 = _____

Home Note: Your child multiplies multiples of 10.

Show What You Know

➤ Write each product.

① 6 × 100 = _____

② 90 × 60 = _____

③ 100 × 9 = _____

④ 70 × 70 = _____

⑤ 600 × 6 = _____

⑥ 20 × 50 = _____

⑦ 400 × 8 = _____

⑧ 600 × 9 = _____

⑨ 500 × 4 = _____

⑩ 300 × 7 = _____

⑪ 30 × 40 = _____

⑫ 80 × 80 = _____

⑬ 200 × 4 = _____

⑭ 60 × 70 = _____

⑮ 500 × 7 = _____

⑯ 90 × 40 = _____

⑰ 5 × 300 = _____

⑱ 700 × 8 = _____

⑲ 50 × 80 = _____

⑳ 4 × 800 = _____

Show What You Know

DIRECTIONS

1		2	3
$\begin{array}{r} 439 \\ \times \quad 5 \end{array}$	$400 \times 5 = 2000$	$\begin{array}{r} 400 \times 5 = 2000 \\ 30 \times 5 = \quad 150 \\ 9 \times 5 = \quad \underline{45} \\ 2195 \end{array}$	✓
Make an estimate.		Multiply and add.	Write a check mark if your answer is close to your estimate.

Make an estimate	Multiply and add	Check estimate
① $\begin{array}{r} 368 \\ \times \ 4 \end{array}$		
② $\begin{array}{r} 842 \\ \times \ 6 \end{array}$		
③ $\begin{array}{r} 588 \\ \times \ 7 \end{array}$		

    Home Note: Your child makes estimates to check the reasonableness of products.

Product Roll

DIRECTIONS

➤ Record your work.
➤ Check your partner's work.

Numbers rolled   _____   _____   _____   _____

Possible problems   × _____   × _____   × _____   × _____

Estimates   _____   _____   _____   _____

Multiplication problem   _____ _____ _____

         ×   _____

     _____ =

     _____ =

     _____ = _____

Home Note: Your child practices multiplying three-digit factors by one-digit factors by playing a game.

Lesson 25

49

Split Both Factors to Multiply

➤ Use the number-splitting strategy to find each product.

1

$$34$$
$$\times\ 45$$

$30 \times 50 = 1500$

Make an estimate.

2

$$34$$
$$\times\ 45$$

30×45 —— $30 \times 40 = 1200$

$30 \times 5 =\ \ \ 150$

4×45 —— $4 \times 40 =\ \ \ 160$

$4 \times 5 =\ \ \ \ 20$

$\overline{1530}$

Split both factors. Multiply. Add.

3

✓

Write a check mark
if your answer
is reasonable.

①

$$29$$
$$\times\ 38$$

②

$$47$$
$$\times\ 56$$

③

$$65$$
$$\times\ 74$$

④

$$83$$
$$\times\ 92$$

Lesson 26

Home Note: Your child multiplies two-digit factors by two-digit factors.

TM & © Scholastic Inc. All rights reserved

Record Fewer Steps

$$
\begin{array}{r}
23 \\
\times\ 48 \\
\hline
\end{array}
$$

1

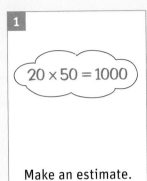

$20 \times 50 = 1000$

Make an estimate.

2

$$
\begin{array}{r}
23 \\
\times\ 48 \\
\hline
20 \times 40 = 800 \\
20 \times 8 =\ \ 160 \\
3 \times 40 =\ \ 120 \\
3 \times 8 =\ \ \ \ 24 \\
\hline
1104
\end{array}
$$

Split both factors. Multiply. Add.

3

Write a check mark
if your answer
is reasonable.

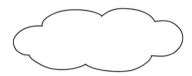

$$
\begin{array}{r}
58 \\
\times\ 24 \\
\hline
\end{array}
$$

Home Note: Your child multiplies two-digit factors by two-digit factors.

Lesson 27

51

Record Fewer Steps

$$\begin{array}{r} 23 \\ \times\ 48 \end{array}$$

1

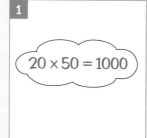

$20 \times 50 = 1000$

Make an estimate.

2

$$\begin{array}{r} 23 \\ \times\ 48 \end{array}$$

$20 \times 40 = 800$
$20 \times 8 = 160$
$3 \times 40 = 120$
$3 \times 8 = 24$
$\overline{1104}$

Split both factors. Multiply. Add.

3

✓

Write a check mark
if your answer
is reasonable.

1

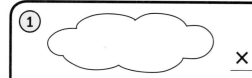

$$\begin{array}{r} 33 \\ \times\ 98 \end{array}$$

2

$$\begin{array}{r} 66 \\ \times\ 74 \end{array}$$

3

$$\begin{array}{r} 25 \\ \times\ 59 \end{array}$$

4

$$\begin{array}{r} 85 \\ \times\ 42 \end{array}$$

Lesson 27

Home Note: Your child multiplies two-digit factors by two-digit factors.

Sometimes You Get Lucky

DIRECTIONS

1

$$\begin{array}{r} 24 \\ \times\ 40 \\ \hline \end{array}$$

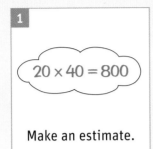

20 × 40 = 800

Make an estimate.

2

$$\begin{array}{r} 24 \\ \times\ 40 \\ 20 \times 40 = 800 \\ 4 \times 40 = \underline{160} \\ 960 \end{array}$$

Split both factors. Multiply. Add.

3

Write a check mark if your answer is reasonable.

①

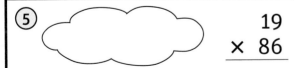

$$\begin{array}{r} 80 \\ \times\ 57 \\ \hline \end{array}$$

②

$$\begin{array}{r} 78 \\ \times\ 20 \\ \hline \end{array}$$

③

$$\begin{array}{r} 51 \\ \times\ 39 \\ \hline \end{array}$$

④

$$\begin{array}{r} 17 \\ \times\ 84 \\ \hline \end{array}$$

⑤

$$\begin{array}{r} 19 \\ \times\ 86 \\ \hline \end{array}$$

⑥

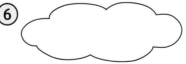

$$\begin{array}{r} 71 \\ \times\ 63 \\ \hline \end{array}$$

Home Note: Your child multiplies two-digit factors by two-digit factors.

Multiplication

➤ Write about what you know and have learned about multiplication.

➤ You may use your class's concept web for ideas.

ABOUT MULTIPLICATION

Home Note: Your child writes about multiplication.

Show What You Know

DIRECTIONS

➤ Write each product.

① 3 × 5 × 2 = _____

② 200 × 4 = _____

③ 2 × 9 × 5 = _____

④ 100 × 32 = _____

⑤ 40 × 6 = _____

⑥ 8 × 300 = _____

⑦ 60 × 80 = _____

⑧ 500 × 8 = _____

⑨ 10 × 29 = _____

⑩ 700 × 6 = _____

⑪ 50 × 70 = _____

⑫ 7 × 300 = _____

➤ Make an estimate and then multiply.

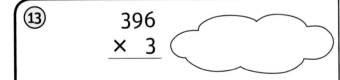

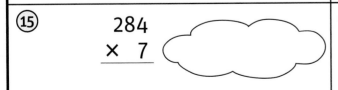

⑬
```
  396
×   3
```

⑭
```
  614
×   6
```

⑮
```
  284
×   7
```

⑯
```
  792
×   4
```

⑰
$$\begin{array}{r} 21 \\ \times\ 36 \\ \hline \end{array}$$

⑱
$$\begin{array}{r} 89 \\ \times\ 50 \\ \hline \end{array}$$

⑲
$$\begin{array}{r} 78 \\ \times\ 32 \\ \hline \end{array}$$

⑳
$$\begin{array}{r} 19 \\ \times\ 43 \\ \hline \end{array}$$

㉑
$$\begin{array}{r} 67 \\ \times\ 91 \\ \hline \end{array}$$

㉒
$$\begin{array}{r} 33 \\ \times\ 29 \\ \hline \end{array}$$

㉓
$$\begin{array}{r} 90 \\ \times\ 74 \\ \hline \end{array}$$

㉔
$$\begin{array}{r} 88 \\ \times\ 39 \\ \hline \end{array}$$

Home Note: Your child solves multiplication problems and multiplies two-digit factors by two-digit factors.

TM & © Scholastic Inc. All rights reserved

Product Roll

➤ Record your work.

➤ Check your partner's work.

Numbers rolled   _____   _____   _____   _____

Possible problems   × _____   × _____   × _____   × _____

Estimates   _____   _____   _____   _____

Multiplication problem   _____ _____ _____

$$\times \quad \underline{\hspace{3cm}} \quad \underline{\hspace{1cm}}$$

_____ =

_____ =

_____ = _____

Home Note: Your child practices multiplying three-digit factors by one-digit factors by playing a game.

Lesson 30

57

Math Vocabulary

> Write new words and terms in the box.
> Write a definition, show an example, or draw a picture for each word or term in your list.

Glossary

Associative Property of Multiplication

When multiplying 3 numbers, the two factors that you multiply first are sometimes said to be grouped together. Grouping different factors to multiply first is an example of the *Associative Property of Multiplication*. To show the grouping, we use parentheses. The parentheses tell you to multiply those two factors first.

For example, to find the product for $2 \times 3 \times 4$ we can group the numbers as $(2 \times 3) \times 4$ or $2 \times (3 \times 4)$.

(2 × 3) × 4 tells us to multiply 2×3 first.

$6 \times 4 = 24$

$2 \times$ *(3 × 4)* tells us to multiply 3×4 first.

$2 \times 12 = 24$

Either way you get the same answer, 24.

Commutative Property of Multiplication

Changing the order of the factors does not change the product. This is called the *Commutative Property of Multiplication*. An example of this property is $3 \times 5 = 5 \times 3$.

equal

Equal means the same amount. For example, twelve is equal to three times four. The symbol for *equal* is $=$.

equation

An *equation* is a number sentence that has an equal sign to show that two amounts have the same value.

For example, $24 = 6 \times 4$ and $5 + 8 = 13$ are *equations*.

estimate (noun)

When you answer the question *"About what will the answer be?"* you make an estimate. An estimate is something you do quickly in your head so that you have an idea about what the exact answer should be close to.

For example, to make an estimate of 57×8 you can think $60 \times 8 = 480$ so 480 is an estimate for 57×8.

factor

Factors are numbers that you multiply to get a product. For example, 3 and 7 are *factors* in the equation $3 \times 7 = 21$.

factor $\times$ *factor* $=$ product

multiple

The product in a multiplication equation is a multiple of the factors. For example, 21 (the product) is a multiple of 3 and a multiple of 7 because $3 \times 7 = 21$.

You can also get a multiple of a number by counting by that number. If you count by 3s and 7s you will say 21 so 21 is a multiple of both 3 and 7.

3, 6, 9, 12, 15, 18, **21**
7, 14, **21**

multiple of 10

Numbers that have a factor of 10 are called *multiples of 10*. They always end in zero. 10, 20, 30, 40, 50, . . . are examples of *multiples of 10*.

multiplication

Multiplication is what you do when you figure the total number of items in equal groups.

multiplication equation

A *multiplication equation* is a number sentence with an equal sign and a times sign. What is on the left side of the equal sign equals what is on the right side.

For example, $18 = 6 \times 3$ and $3 \times 4 = 2 \times 6$ are both multiplication equations.

Multiplication Property of One

The product of any number and 1 is the number. For example, 7×1 and 1×7 both equal 7.

multiply

When you multiply, you find the product of factors or the total number of items in equal groups. For example, if you multiply 5 and 2, you get the product 10.

product

A *product* is the answer you get when you multiply factors. For example, 21 is the *product* in the equation $3 \times 7 = 21$.

square number

A *square number* is the product of a number times itself. You can show that a number is a square number if you can take that number of tiles and form a square.

For example, 16 is a *square number* because it is the product of 4×4 and you can form a square with 16 tiles.

symbols

You use *symbols* in mathematics to name numbers $\left(12, 308, \frac{1}{2} \right)$, operations $(+, -, \times, \div)$, and relationships between numbers $(=, >, <)$.

times

The word *times* between numbers tells you to multiply the numbers. Four times two means you should figure the product of 4 and 2 or figure how many in 4 groups of 2. The symbol for times is $\times$.

Zero Property of Multiplication

The product of any number and zero is zero. For example, 0×7 and 7×0 both equal 0.

Multiplication Chart

X	1	2	3	4	5	6	7	8	9	10	11	12
1	1	2	3	4	5	6	7	8	9	10	11	12
2	2	4	6	8	10	12	14	16	18	20	22	24
3	3	6	9	12	15	18	21	24	27	30	33	36
4	4	8	12	16	20	24	28	32	36	40	44	48
5	5	10	15	20	25	30	35	40	45	50	55	60
6	6	12	18	24	30	36	42	48	54	60	66	72
7	7	14	21	28	35	42	49	56	63	70	77	84
8	8	16	24	32	40	48	56	64	72	80	88	96
9	9	18	27	36	45	54	63	72	81	90	99	108
10	10	20	30	40	50	60	70	80	90	100	110	120
11	11	22	33	44	55	66	77	88	99	110	121	132
12	12	24	36	48	60	72	84	96	108	120	132	144